MAKING THE GRADE *P*REPARATORY GRADE

EASY POPULAR PIECES FOR YOUNG PIANISTS. SELECTED AND ARRANGED BY JERRY LANNING

Exclusive distributors: Music Sales Limited,
Newmarket Road, Bury St. Edmunds, Suffolk IP33 3YB.
This book © Copyright 2001 Chester Music Ltd
ISBN 0-7119-9099-9
Order No. CH63602

Cover design and typesetting by Pemberton & Whitefoord
Printed in the United Kingdom by
Caligraving Limited, Thetford, Norfolk.

Chester Music

(A division of Music Sales Limited)
8/9 Frith Street, London W1D 3JB.

INTRODUCTION

This revised and updated collection of 15 popular tunes provides additional attractive teaching repertoire to complement the first books in the MAKING THE GRADE series. As with the previous books, the pieces have been carefully arranged and graded and the collection is made up of well-known material which pupils will enjoy. The standard of pieces progresses from beginner to Associated Board Preparatory Grade.

CONTENTS

MICHAEL, ROW THE BOAT ASHORE

Traditional

This tune uses six notes, but as you only have five fingers you need to change hand position sometimes.
This is done by changing fingers on the repeated note G in bars 4/5 and 12/13.

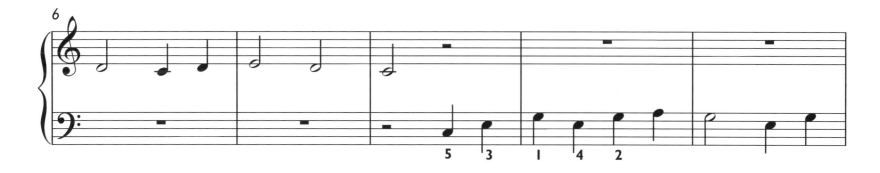

EDELWEISS

Words by Oscar Hammerstein II
Music by Richard Rodgers

Notice the key signature and remember to sharpen all the Fs. Be sure to count three full beats for all the dotted crotchets.

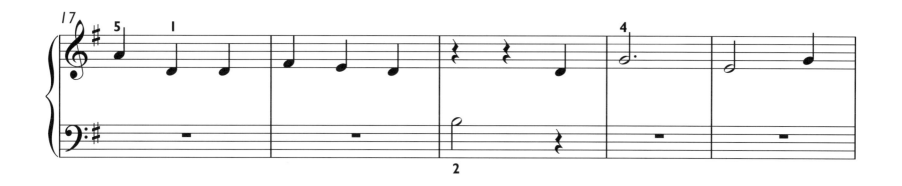

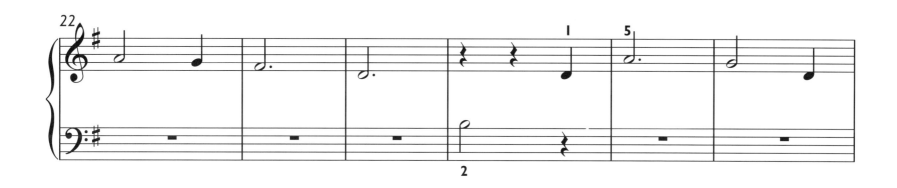

ANY DREAM WILL DO

Music by Andrew Lloyd Webber
Words by Tim Rice

Take care that you don't hold notes on through the crotchet rests.

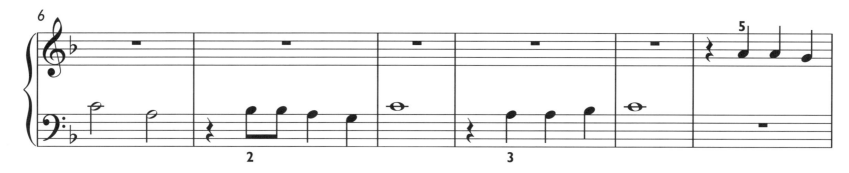

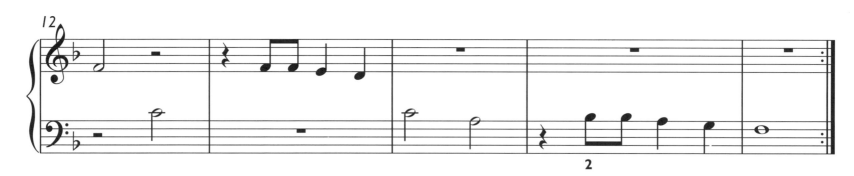

AMERICAN PIE

Words and Music by Don McLean

Your hands should take over smoothly from each other without a break.

Quite quickly ♩ = 88

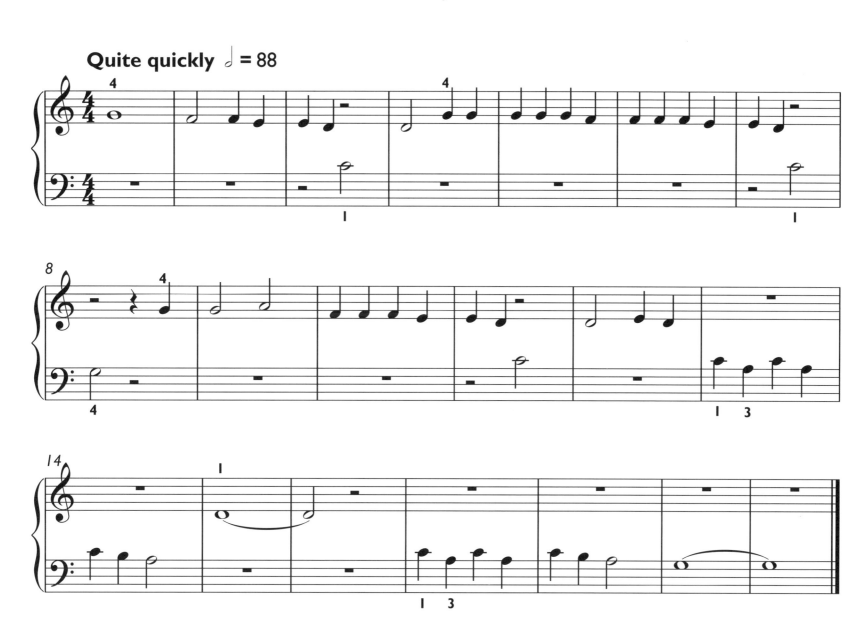

JUPITER

By Gustav Holst

This very famous tune comes from Holst's orchestral suite "The Planets".
Watch out for the changes of hand position.

Majestically ♩ = 68

THE BLUE DANUBE

by Johann Strauss II

This tune is a waltz, a graceful dance popular in the nineteenth century.
Take care you give the rests on the second beat of the bar their full value.

With a lilt ♩ = 144

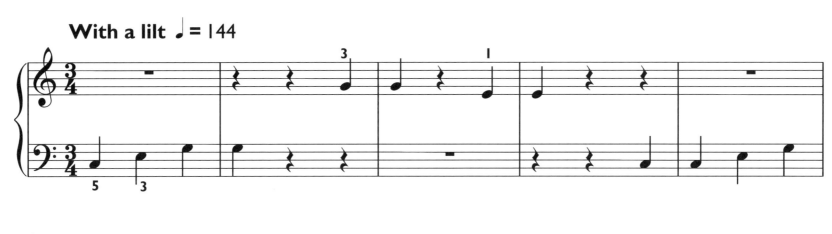

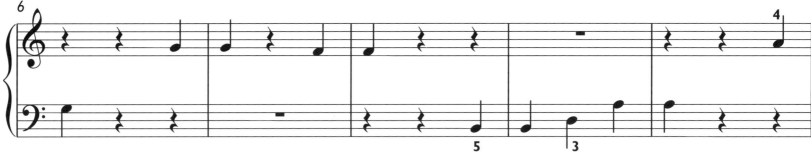

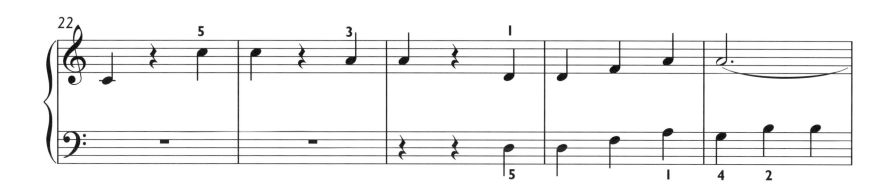

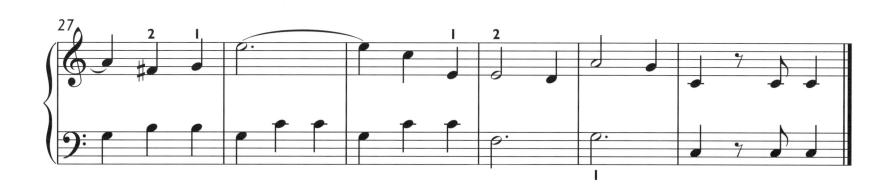

BARBIE GIRL

Words and Music by Soren Rasted, Claus Norreen, Rene Dif, Lene Nystrom, Johnny Pederson & Karsten Delgado

In bars 15 and 16 change finger in the left hand while holding down the note.
Be sure to count the last two bars very carefully.

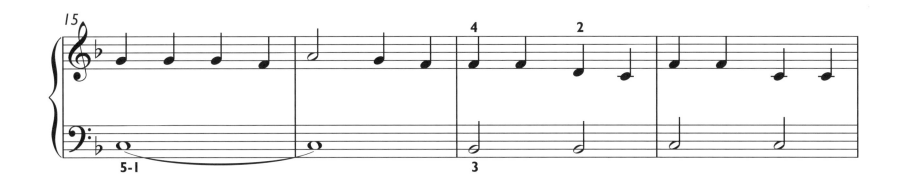

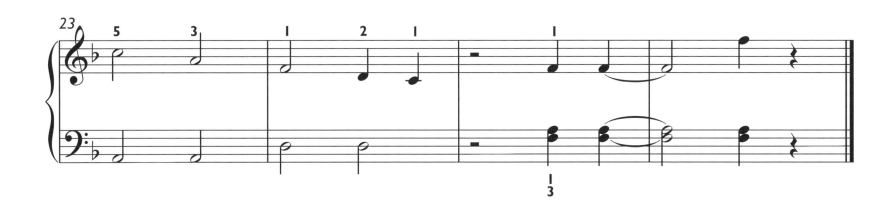

OOM PAH PAH

Words and Music by Lionel Bart

This jolly song is from the musical "Oliver".
Practise the last line carefully and notice the accidentals.

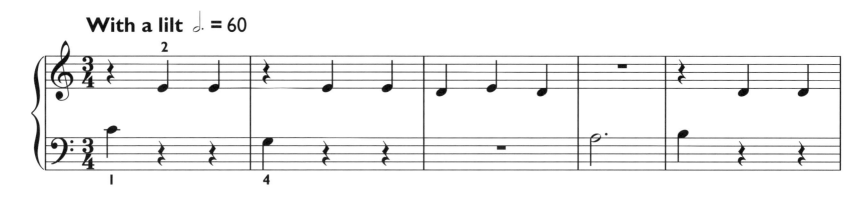

WHEN THE SAINTS GO MARCHING IN

Traditional

Keep a steady tempo, counting four in each bar.
Notice that the piece starts on the second beat of the bar, not the first.

MY OWN HOME

(From Walt Disney Pictures' "The Jungle Book")

Words and Music by Richard M. Sherman & Robert B. Sherman

Play this song from "The Jungle Book" as smoothly and expressively as possible.

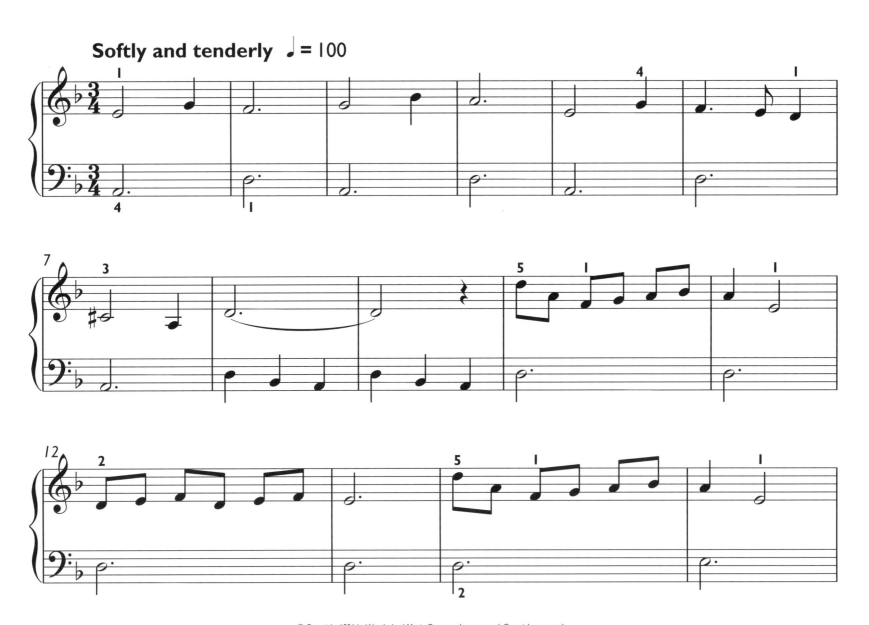

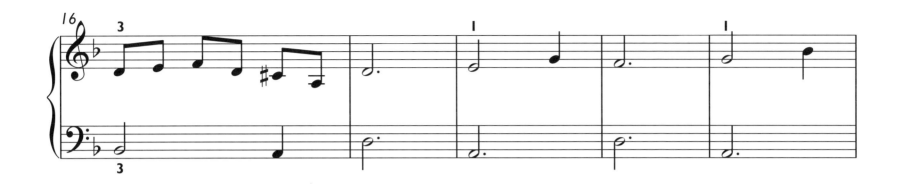

HEY, HEY, ARE YOU READY TO PLAY?

(Tweenies Theme)

Words by Graham Pike & Liz Kitchen
Music by Will Brenton & Ian Lauchlan

Notice the signs *mf* and *f*. What do they mean?

Quite brightly ♩ = 128

I WAN'NA BE LIKE YOU

(From Walt Disney Pictures' "The Jungle Book")

Words and Music by Richard M. Sherman and Robert B. Sherman

Remember that *all* the Gs are sharpened, because the effect of the sharp sign lasts right through the bar.

ALL THROUGH THE NIGHT

Traditional

All the notes under each slur (phrase mark) should be joined smoothly together.

MI CHICO LATINO

Words and Music by Geri Halliwell, Andy Watkins & Paul Wilson

Practise the right hand on its own at first, and take care with repeated quavers.

COLONEL HATHI'S MARCH

(From Walt Disney Pictures' "The Jungle Book")

Words and Music by Richard M. Sherman and Robert B. Sherman

Pay attention to the rests in the left hand, but still take care to play the right hand smoothly.

4/06(58669)